A World-Class Production System

Lessons of 20 Years in Pursuit of World Class

A WORLD-CLASS PRODUCTION SYSTEM

Lessons of 20 Years in Pursuit of World Class

JOHN R. BLACK

Viva Books Private Limited

New Delhi • Mumbai • Chennai • Kolkata • Bangalore

First Indian Edition 2004

VIVA BOOKS PRIVATE LIMITED

- 4262/3 Ansari Road, Daryaganj, New Delhi 110 002
  E-mail: viva@vivagroupindia.net

- 215-216 New Apollo Estate, 2nd Floor, Mogra Lane, Andheri (E),
  Mumbai 400 069 E-mail: vivamumbai@vivagroupindia.net

- 7 Aziz Mulk, Seventh Street, Thousand Lights, Chennai 600 006
  E-mail: vivachennai@vivagroupindia.net

- B–103, Jindal Towers, 21/1A/3, Darga Road, Kolkata 700 017
  E-mail: vivakolkata@vivagroupindia.net

- 7 Sovereign Park Apts., 56-58 K. R. Road, Basavanagudi,
  Bangalore 560 004 Email: vivabangalore@vivagroupindia.net

Published by arrangement with

Crisp Publications. Inc.
1200 Hamilton Court,
Menlo Park
CA 94025
USA

ISBN 81-7649-670-7

Published by Vinod Vasishtha for Viva Books Private Limited, 4262/3 Ansari Road, Daryaganj, New Delhi 110 002 and printed at Raj Press, R-3 Inderpuri, New Delhi – 110012.

This book is dedicated to all the workers
at Boeing who work hard and never give up.

The lessons learned detailed in this book are invaluable to everyone undertaking major process change. In his work, John shares and celebrates real life successes, the commercial aerospace industry's struggle to change and it's attempts to understand and not repeat failed experiences. Underlying it all, he reminds us that empowered and educated people, in conjunction with committed leadership, are the catalysts that enable the transformation to take place. This book represents a practical guide toward implementing a lean manufacturing system.

Carolyn Corvi
Vice President, General Manager
Aircraft Systems and Interiors
Boeing Commercial Airplane Group
The Boeing Company

Here is the story, from the soldier on the front line, of the continuing efforts of Boeing to remake itself in the image of Toyota. It's not a pretty story–real stories about fundamental change never are–but it's an honest story told with great enthusiasm and deep knowledge of what must be done. Anyone trying to transform a vast organization from mass production to lean thinking will find a wealth of lessons here on what to do and when to do it.

James Womack
Co-author, The Machine That Changed the World
Co-author, Lean Thinking

In this very readable book about lean manufacturing, John Black has focused attention on the key aspect of how to make an organization lean. He clearly understands and explains that the secret is all in the people: "Real competitive advantage is in how we develop and focus human potential in the way we do business."

Art Byrne
President
The Wiremold Company

In this lesson-based overview of World-Class Production, the significance of true employee empowerment and employee development shines through. John Black consistently reminds us of the connection between genuine involvement of people who do the real work and the ability of the organization to achieve amazing results.

Kathleen Ryan
President, The Orion Partnership
Lead author, Driving Fear Out of the Workplace
Co-author, The Courageous Messenger

For any business to succeed in this highly competitive global environment, relentless pursuit of this book's ten lessons for World-Class Production is absolutely mandatory.

Chuck Kahler
Vice President
Wing Responsibility Center
Boeing Commercial Airplane Group
The Boeing Company

Contents

PREFACE

I have learned much about people and the way work is done in my two decades at Boeing. It has been a journey that has taken me all over the world. I believe the journey has formally concluded at the intersection of People, Lean Principles, and the Toyota Production System. My visits to Japan, in grease up to my elbows on the factory floor on my learn/do excursions, have given me the understanding that striving for perfection is a way of life. I know perfection is achieved by many small improvements made continuously. The simple truth is that focusing on the long term drives us to focus on the present, rather than the past or future. And the present is where we need to be to replace mental models about the relationship of people, materials and machines in how the work gets done by people.

The individual has always been at the center of U.S. society, but at Boeing we've learned that people in a team are the "power" and "enablers" to create a world-class production system. The core of this vision is the fundamental belief in people and people-building. People must change the paradigms. When changes come from the work itself, as instigated by the people who do that work, organizations change naturally. Structures change from hierarchical to flat. So people working in the factory or office evolve to high performance teams as a result or out of the empowerment of the world-class production system. And costs get reduced and profits multiply providing the target is the identification and elimination of waste.

The capacity to adapt to change is a fundamental, if seldom recognized, ingredient in Toyota's success, as it must be in other companies. The "All American Kentuckians" at Toyota of Georgetown are contributors to Toyota's $21 billion in cash and short-term securities. They are a team of great diversity from varied educational backgrounds. They will tell you:

- We have been given the authority to stop the line . . . "we don't pass on defects."
- Our system takes an incredible amount of detailed planning, discipline, hard work, and painstaking attention to detail.
- We work like dancers in a choreographed production: retrieving parts, installing them, checking the quality, and doing it all in immaculate surroundings.
- Our great strength is in our ability to learn. We are problem-conscious and customer-oriented, and this preparedness is the source of our company's dynamic capability.
- We can develop a car in 18 months or less, and we don't make the same mistake twice.

I strongly believe giving people the expectation of "empowerment" in a system replete with waste and under a "thumb" of autocratic management or computing complexity is unjust. People working to build world-class products have a right to demand the environment that allows them to work in a Kaizen-based system that gives them the authority to identify and eliminate the waste and continuously strive for perfection.

To all my associates in Boeing I would like to express my thanks and appreciation. We have travelled far and learned much on our road to world-class production, as described in this book. All of us, together, make our progress possible. To get this story into words, I would like especially to thank Amy Bradshaw, of Boeing, for her much-needed and valued help in editing my manuscript.

The Boeing Company that we are working to change and improve isn't just today's Boeing. It is a company that will last through all of our lifetimes and those of our children. Management everywhere must learn to embrace a long-term view with the consciousness that what we do today is part of a continually improving process. It is never done. I hope this short book helps get you started in that direction.

I.

BACKGROUND— WHAT IS A WORLD-CLASS PRODUCTION SYSTEM?

LESSON 1: PEOPLE ARE THE KEY TO WORLD CLASS, NOT TECHNOLOGY.

You should submit wisdom to the company. If you don't have any wisdom to contribute, submit sweat. If nothing else, work hard and don't sleep. Or resign.

Taiichi Ohno

I SAT IN THE CLASSROOM listening to Yoshiki Iwata, Presi-dent of Shingijutsu, as he addressed another group of business leaders from around the world. This was my fourth in a series of trips to expose managers to the principles of world-class production, and Iwata was teaching us about Just In Time (JIT), the production system his protégé Taiichi Ohno pioneered at Toyota Motors.

My mind drifted back to 1967, when I was an infantry advisor to the South Vietnamese army. In a speech at Fort Gordon, Georgia, Dr. Bernard Fall told us "Technology doesn't win wars, people do. Soldiers do." A balance of people and technology, I realized, is still the key to both military and production victory.

What a great message, a simple message that has been taken up and put into practice now at Boeing and at other great companies everywhere. While technology and most industries go hand-in-hand, companies all over the world struggle to strike the balance between people and technology. And one of the first truths faced in trying to change company cultures is that although many companies build great products, so do their competitors. They work hard on research and development, but so do their competitors. No one can claim a monopoly or even a significant advantage in technology.

More than 100 managers from around the world took notes as Iwata shared lessons from his life with JIT. They would soon practice the techniques themselves on the shop floor during a two-day Kaizen event at Hitachi led by consultants from Shingijutsu, who specialize in helping companies develop JIT production systems. The following week Mr. Iwata's consultants would take the managers on tours of companies that have implemented JIT production.

It is a powerful learn/do experience. The managers learn the concept of Kaizen, continuous improvement essential for achieving Just In Time production. Many companies require them to participate in Kaizen within a few weeks of returning home. To change the management culture, companies are shifting from classroom studies to hands-on, action-oriented learning.

Produce Only What We Need

"Taiichi Ohno," recounted Iwata, "said we needed to do something extraordinary to compete, to produce efficiently. We needed to reduce the input and produce the same output to improve efficiency and productivity. Taiichi Ohno thought the only efficient way was to produce what was needed. In most cases, though, companies make more than what is needed. We add extra: we 'overproduce.'

"In addition, we deliver too quickly. Such a system of cushioned quantities and schedules makes warehouses necessary to store goods made in excess quantities and delivered too early."

"Companies I have visited produce more than what is needed, and have inventory, but still miss deliveries. Because of this wasteful situation we need Just In Time."

This strict philosophy demands that we know how to get our workforce to produce what is needed, in the amount needed, when it is needed.

Field a Team of Multi-Skilled Players

Mr. Iwata concluded his teaching session: "People *are* multi-skilled, but suddenly when they go to work they develop the habit of only doing one thing. Can you evenly divide the time between different jobs that need to be done? The answer is 'no.' You cannot do it because of the great variability between many human operations."

"You need multiple-skilled people. They need to be able to do three jobs–their own jobs, the previous job and the next job." Just In Time, then, is not just about inventory scheduling.

Just In Time Production: The Secret Weapon

Just In Time is not new. Our ancestors have employed JIT production throughout history to ensure survival and victory. Indeed, humans improve production techniques because our victory, success and survival depend on them.

In the late sixteenth century, the Republic of Venice developed the world's first large-scale assembly line and industrial plant. The plant built warships, and sometimes set 100 ships afloat in just six weeks. This phenomenal output resulted from production techniques that we would praise as highly effective even by today's standards.

Two centuries later, production of weapons again confirmed the value of effective manufacturing systems. George Washington awarded Eli Whitney a contract to manufacture muskets. To provide high-quality muskets quickly to Washington's forces, Whitney's factory used advanced production techniques such as ordered and integrated workflow, standard interchangeable parts, focused factory areas, dedicated machines and minimal product variations.

The concept of lean manufacturing so earnestly studied by American industry today derives mainly from the Toyota production system, which will serve as a model throughout this book.

Our Competitive Advantage Is Us

Since my career at Boeing began in 1978, I've seen a lot of changes as well as a lot of things that never seem to change. My job has been to learn from the best and the brightest in the world, to help create the vision of world-class production, and to help get the vision implemented.

I've come to the conclusion that real competitive advantage is in how we develop and focus human potential in the way we do business. And developing and focusing human potential is not an easy process.

It's difficult for managers used to the old autocratic ways of management by control to change. It's difficult to simplify long-entrenched bureaucratic processes. It's difficult to flatten and streamline organizations as those involved fight desperately to protect turf.

It's difficult to earn the trust of employees and genuinely empower them to make needed changes and improvements. I'm talking about the empowerment that counts the most: the freedom to challenge and to change standard operating procedures, workflow design and bureaucratic processes. This is the freedom most often denied first-level employees. All of these things challenge us. But difficulty should not dissuade us from embarking on a journey that can yield such rich rewards. Many have gone before us and prevailed.

Beginning the Journey to World Class

Shortly after I joined Boeing, I became a student of Dr. Juran and Dr. Deming and helped introduce their principles around the company.

Dr. Deming advised our management that they must know exactly what to do, and to involve the workers to get the answer.

In early 1985, Dr. Juran, in a meeting with the president of the Boeing Aerospace Company, stressed that the key to management innovation is the pursuit of total quality. That pivotal meeting acquainted the company with Juran's teachings. The results of this early work with the ideas of Juran, Deming, and others laid the groundwork for our journey toward world class.

Waste You Can See

One of the first Boeing executives to implement Juran and Deming's idea was Bill Selby. In 1987, he dumped 15 million dollars worth of waste collected over 90 days on the factory floor and then talked about it with an audience of 4,000 employees in the Everett plant. Employees all over Boeing still talk about that speech, in which Selby observed, "It is the system management has put in place that created the waste, not the people doing the work." And he was right.

Before you can start to put a world-class production system in place, you must identify concrete examples of material waste. Then, get started on waste reduction. These efforts will lead to effective cost-cutting and solid process improvements. Ultimately, both survival and success depend on it.

Waste That Is Hard to See

But the biggest waste is not the material Selby had strewn on the factory floor. It is waste that is harder to see (see Figure 1). It is the failure to leverage resources.

Manufacturing industries tend to rely on more technology for improved profitability. Companies in America build more factories and new equipment, and search high and low for costly, high-tech solutions or improvements.

But history tells us again and again that the biggest resource available to companies is not technology, it is people. The failure to leverage the power of people is the greatest single source of waste. Focusing on people instead of technology, and empowering them to use their potential, is the key to world-class competitiveness. A strong team of people–machinists, analysts, engineers, vice presidents, middle management, secretaries, etc.–can get rid of the waste.

1. **Waste of overproduction**
2. **Waste of time**
3. **Waste of transportation**
4. **Waste of processing itself**
5. **Waste of inventory**
6. **Waste of motion**
7. **Waste of making defective products**

Figure 1. Taiichi Ohno's Seven Wastes

Beauty of Simplicity

As simple as that may sound, it's one of the hardest lessons for companies to learn. It's been a tough lesson for many companies. Why? Because it's simple, and we tend to think that solutions should be complicated. However, just because it's a *simple* truth doesn't mean it's an *easy* one to follow.

Making the most of people allows a company to become increasingly leaner and to pursue stretch goals and strategies. Taking a stretch approach to business literally means "lean everything." A company can't begin to achieve "lean everything" without developing and focusing the potential of people.

Compliance Is Not Commitment

Along with the challenge of empowering people to reduce waste, another lesson many companies learn with great pain is the difference between compliance and commitment.

In the 1980s and the early 1990s, North American companies spent years complying with quality principles but weren't quite committed to them. They didn't really begin to change the way they did business until they actually put the education, the theorizing, the philosophizing and the campaigning into a real-life work situation. Compliance is nice, but only commitment succeeds.

Compliance is going through the appropriate *motions,* but commitment results from the appropriate *emotions.* The distinction explains why some companies succeed in turning things around and why other companies do not.

Commitment is rooted in deep conviction, a passion or belief about something. There is, and must be, a sense of urgency about commitment to motivate and inspire people to action.

The New Frontier: People

That takes us back to the need to strike the right balance between people and technology. Technology alone doesn't win competitive wars. The right technology applied by people at the lowest level who are empowered to design and decide its application is the critical difference.

The "new frontier" for competitive advantage is people, not technology. The companies most successful in aerospace and other industries are those that best cultivate and focus human potential. I truly believe it's that simple.

Committing wholly to the goal of relying on human potential as a central corporate strategy requires courage, ingenuity, integrity and a passion for the human spirit. Not many companies are able to make that commitment. Fewer still can honor it in ways that work. But the few that do both are enormously successful.

Boeing's commitments began with an emphasis on learning. From 1990 to 1991, seven missions including 100 of our top executives visited Japan to tour the Toyota Motor Company and many other companies. Our executives saw the world-class production system in Japan. They came back with a new vision of what "world class" is, and got started implementing it. They didn't wait around: they knew what to do and started doing it. Simple.

In the chapters that follow, I will share some of the key lessons I have learned in 20 years on the continuing journey to world class.

II.

Getting Lean—The Route to World-Class Production

Lesson 2: If You Are Going Uphill and Taking One Step at a Time, You Are Headed in the Right Direction.

MANY COMPANIES ARE PLOTTING A COURSE toward becoming a World-Class Enterprise. Not many, however, understand that a world-class production system is neither new nor easy to implement. Companies that are successful world-class manufacturing operations, like Toyota, accomplished it one arduous step at a time. There is no such thing as becoming a world-class company overnight, and no such thing as becoming world class at all without a Kaizen-based tool in every employee's belt. Because world-class manufacturing is centrally concerned with actual production processes, culture change is not enough.

Henry Ford: The Father of Cycle Time Management

Henry Ford hated to waste time. In 1926 he wrote, "Time waste differs from material waste in that there can be no salvage. The easiest of all wastes, and the hardest to correct, is the waste of time, because wasted time does not litter the floor like wasted material." Between 1913 and 1914, Ford doubled production with no increase in the workforce. Between 1920 and 1926, cycle time or production lead time was reduced by 90 percent, from 21 days to 2 days.

The secret to Ford's success in creating a new process model for automobile manufacturing was Continuous Flow Assembly. Although his emergency was not a military one, remember that Ford was trying to build and dominate a brand-new industry. He was quite literally trying to change the world. Like the other precursors of world-class manufacturing, Ford implemented world-class methods to survive and prevailed, this time in the commercial battlefield.

Toyota Production System

Similar to but stricter than Ford's original production system, the Toyota Production System is founded on two basic requirements.

- First, top management must make a strong, visible commitment to the system, and must participate directly in implementing it. Additionally, middle management must be instructed to do likewise.

- All employees must participate in the system.

Full participation is essential because the Toyota Production System works by establishing a smooth, continuous flow through the entire production sequence.

The Toyota system is not for the apathetic. It pressures both managers and employees to stay involved and vigilant in making improvements. This pressure, however, makes for a stimulating workplace where managers and employees can take charge of their collective destiny.

The Toyota system is a Just-In-Time production system. It starts with the customer. All production activity is linked to sales in the marketplace. Assembly plants make vehicles only in response to actual dealer orders. Each process arrays items for following processes to withdraw and use only as needed. Each process withdraws items from the preceding process only to make items to replace ones that the following process has withdrawn.

One important aspect of this JIT system is leveled production. A variety of body types move along the same assembly line at the same time. The production of different body types is staggered evenly over the course of the day. This makes the most efficient use of people and equipment. Leveling production allows the pattern of production to follow the pattern of sales. It also prevents a disproportionate burden being imposed on one team at a time while other teams are idle.

Figure 2. Push and pull production

The Toyota system is a pull system (see Figure 2). All production is linked to real demand. Everything that happens is a response to fulfilling actual orders from dealers.

Toyota operates using *kanban.* Kanban are printed cards in clear plastic cases (see Figure 3). Every item or set of items that flows through the production system carries its own kanban. Kanban come off of items that have been used or transported and go back to the preceding process as orders for additional items.

Toyota uses two kinds of kanban: parts withdrawal kanban and production instruction kanban. Withdrawal kanban communicate between processes and production instruction kanban communicate inside processes. Employees use kanban to continuously monitor the material they withdraw from the preceding processes and the finished items they pass on to the next process. Every large assembly shop at Toyota has two or more kanban stations. Paperwork is minimized and efficiency is maximized.

Continuous Flow Production

Toyota arranges equipment in a single, smooth flow. Work within each process is arranged to flow smoothly from one step to the next. Logistics move the work smoothly and on a precise schedule from raw materials plants through machining plants to assembly plants and on to distributors, dealers and customers.

Kanban Cards

Can be used for production and between supplier and factory, as well as between processes.

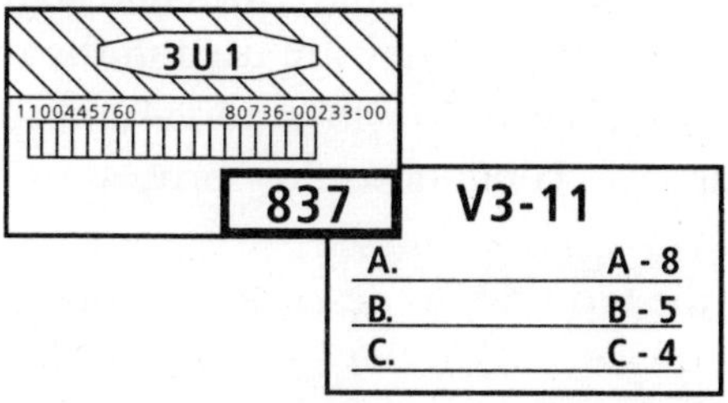

Boxes containing parts can also be kanbans themselves: when they are empty, they are returned as a signal to make or provide more parts.

Signal kanbans are especially useful in the case of large quantity parts.

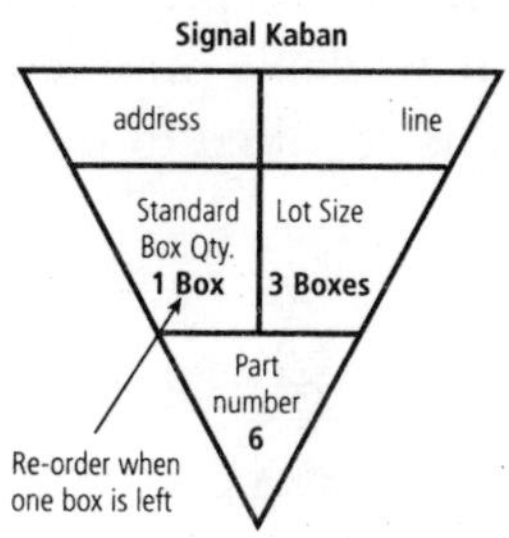

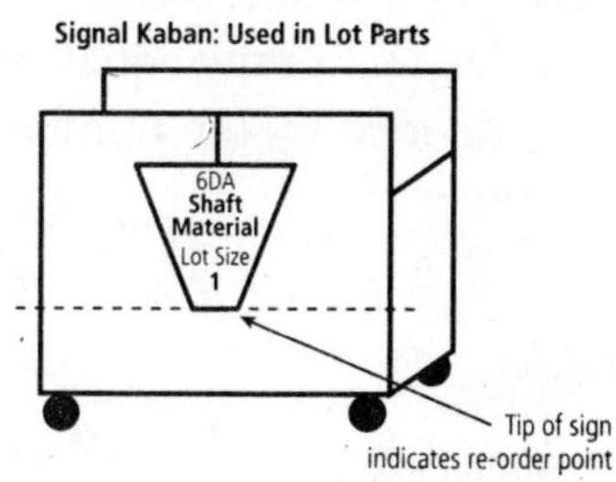

Signal kanbans show the order point in stacks of containers. When the re-order box is reached, the kanban comes off and signals replenishment.

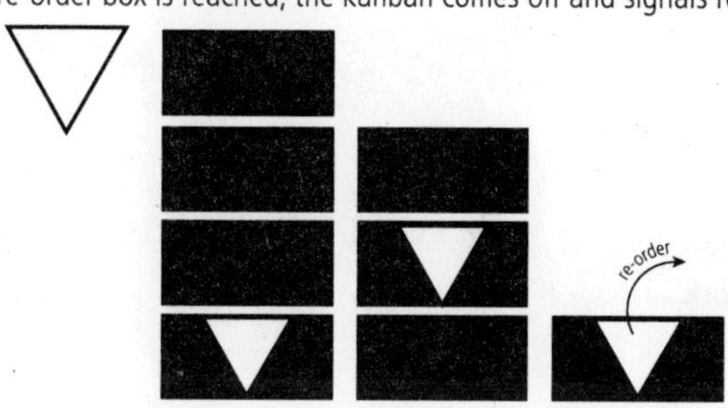

Figure 3. Examples of kanban

Instead of grouping all machines together by type of machine, with all of the lathes together, all of the milling machines together, and so on, Toyota arranges the machines in the order that they are used in the manufacturing process. This means low inventories and small lot sizes which improves continuous flow processing (see Figure 4).

Toyota uses the term *takt* to describe the pace of sales in the marketplace. Takt is the German word for meter. It is quantified in Toyota plants as the quotient of daily working hours divided by the number of vehicle orders to fulfill each day. According to this quotient, takt times are worked out for each item used to produce the vehicles. Takt time equals the total available production time divided by the number of units required to meet customer demand.

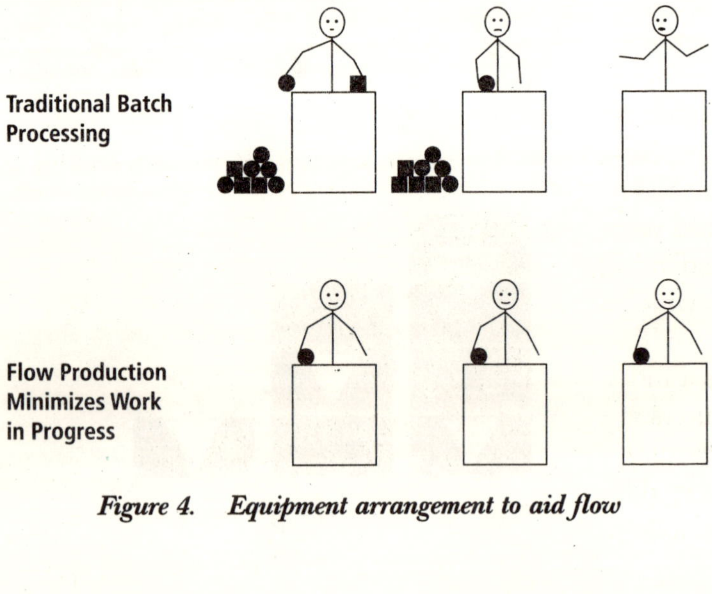

Figure 4. Equipment arrangement to aid flow

Toyota also relies on multi-skilled workers to further improve continuous flow. Once a takt time is determined, work is allocated to maintain a steady, optimal workload for each operator and each machine. Multi-skilled operators give Toyota the flexibility to assign work precisely according to takt times, but without overloading individual workers.

Jidoka is another important principle at Toyota. This is the principle of stopping work immediately whenever a problem arises. Toyota production equipment stops automatically whenever abnormalities occur. Workers halt the line when defects are suspected. This prevents defects from proceeding any further into the system, and also helps identify the causes of problems by halting the line as soon as a problem is identified.

The Toyota production system strives for standardized work. This keeps productivity, quality and safety at high levels. It also provides a consistent framework for performing work at designated takt times, and for illuminating opportunities for improving work procedures.

Toyota incorporates revolutionary changes in automobile manufacturing. Kaizen improvements in standardized work help maximize productivity by encouraging individuals to help design, manage and improve their own jobs.

Today, Toyota dominates the automobile market and is a model for manufacturing excellence. Many manufacturers are trying to follow Toyota's example, and they're learning that a world-class operation is highly efficient but very difficult to achieve. Toyota's example is not that easy to follow.

Lean Thinking

Before you start to think about how Toyota's system applies to your business, you must understand lean thinking.

Lean thinking is a new paradigm. World-class production requires less of everything compared to mass production. As noted by James Womack and Daniel T. Jones in their book *Lean Thinking*[1], "lean" means

- half the human effort in the factory
- half the manufacturing space
- half the investment in tools
- half the engineering hours to develop a new product in half the time

The inventory required on site is far less than half. Lean means fewer defects and the ability to produce a greater variety of products.

When your enterprise has achieved these "half" reductions, you should again try to reduce by half. This sort of lean thinking–the belief that you can always find more waste to cut away–will lead you to a world-class production system.

The Important Number: Zero

Understanding these basics of world-class production is necessary in making the shift to a world-class paradigm. The world-class paradigm is outside of most companies' thinking and far outside of their comfort zone. The World-Class Paradigm = Zero.

Zero means zero defects, zero changeover, zero inventory, even zero quality control. Such goals are basic to world-class production. Zero suggests both a bull's-eye or target value, and an aggressive agenda for improvement.

The Nine Zeros of World-Class Production:

1. ZERO customer dissatisfaction
2. ZERO misalignment
3. ZERO bureaucracy
4. ZERO stakeholder dissatisfaction
5. ZERO lost information
6. ZERO waste
7. ZERO non-value-adding work
8. ZERO breakdowns
9. ZERO lost opportunity

World-class production starts by removing all waste from production, and then goes much further. It also focuses on removing all waste from the organizational structure and from management practices. It is aggressively customer-focused–and customer focus is nothing less than eliminating customer dissatisfaction by knowing and serving the customer well.

Leading World Class: A Tall Order

Leadership's job under world-class production is to plan carefully and execute flawlessly, to avoid misalignment of goals. The system fights bureaucracy by empowering employees and managing through teams. The culture of empowerment eliminates waste by instilling a mindset of waste elimination. All non-value-added work is eliminated. World-class maintenance strives to eradicate breakdowns and all equipment-related loss. And finally, world-class engineering eliminates lost opportunities to respond to market changes.

III.

Japanese Roots—Toyota, Toyota, Toyota

Lesson 3: Without the Understanding and Knowledge of the Toyota Production System, You Are a Small Ship in Heavy Fog without a Reliable Compass.

Learning about world class is certainly an international endeavor. Japan in particular has pioneered the systems that, if correctly used, can increase output while minimizing input. Japan has also shown us an example of the strict system's success. This means the system works in any industry or business large or small.

Starting with the Loom

The world standard today for efficient production is the Toyota Production System pioneered early in the twentieth century by Sakichi Toyoda, his son Kiichiro Toyoda, and a production engineer by the name of Taiichi Ohno.

Sakichi Toyoda, the inventor of automatic looms, founded the Toyota Group. In 1902 he came up with a loom that stopped automatically if any of the threads snapped (see Figure 5).

His invention opened the way for automated loomworks that enabled a single operator to handle dozens of looms. Because a loom would not continue to produce imperfect fabric and use up thread after a problem occurred, Sakichi's invention reduced defects and raised yields. This principle of designing equipment to stop automatically and call attention to problems immediately is a cornerstone of the Toyota production system.

When the Toyota Group set up an automobile manufacturing operation in the 1930s, Sakichi's son, Kiichiro, headed the new venture. Kiichiro traveled to the United States to study Henry Ford's production operations. He returned to Japan with an understanding of Ford's conveyor system, which he was determined to adapt to the small production volumes of the Japanese market.

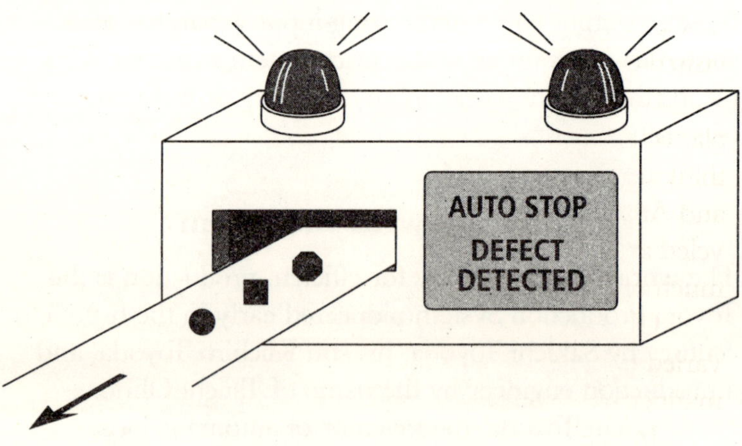

Figure 5. Machines that can stop automatically

In Japan, the young Toyoda implemented Ford's conveyor system. And he organized production of the different parts needed in the assembly sequence to produce and supply them only in the varieties and quantities necessary and only when needed. In this way, each process produced only that which was required by the next process. Having designed and put into use this basic philosophical foundation, Toyoda coined the term "Just In Time."

From the Supermarket: World-Class Production

Taiichi Ohno made the integrated framework of the Toyota Production System a reality. In the late 1940s, Ohno, who later became an executive vice president at Toyota, managed a machining shop. He experimented with ways of configuring the equipment to produce needed items in a timely manner. But he got an entirely new perspective on his JIT production system when he visited the United States in 1956.

Ohno went to the United States to visit automobile plants, but it was the supermarkets that influenced his thinking. Japan did not have many self-service stores yet, and American grocery stores impressed Ohno. He marveled at the way customers chose exactly what and how much of a commodity they wanted (see Figure 6).

Ohno admired the way the supermarkets supplied varied merchandise in a simple, efficient and timely manner.

In later years, Ohno often described his production system in terms of the American supermarket. Each production line arrayed its diverse output for the following

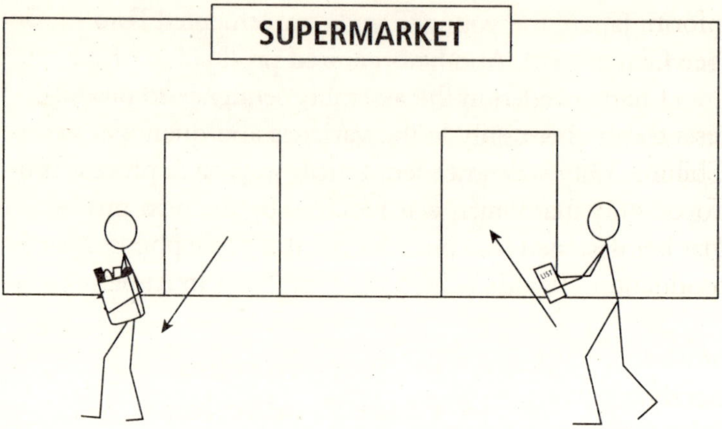

Figure 6. Supermarkets

line to choose from, like merchandise on supermarket shelves. Each line became the customer for the preceding line as well as the supermarket for the subsequent line. The upstream line would come and choose the items it needed and take only those items. Then the preceding line would produce only the replacement items for those that the following line had selected.

Ohno's industrial supermarket concept, then, was a pull system, activated and defined by the needs of the downstream customer.

Taiichi Ohno's Legacy

Ohno developed a number of tools for operating his production format in a systematic framework. The best known of those tools is the kanban system, which conveys information in and between processes on instruction cards. (See Chapter 2 for more about kanban.)

Ohno's legacy of controlled production improvement rests today in the hands of his protégés Yoshiki Iwata and Chihiro Nakao. Both of these men eventually retired from Toyota to form Shingijutsu Ltd., a consulting company that helps other companies implement world-class production.

Iwata and Nakao are the leading current emissaries of what the Japanese have learned about producing efficiently and with the highest possible quality. Their pioneering endeavors into better manufacturing methods and continuous quality improvement are unquestionably world class. The closer companies get to emulating their accomplishments, the closer they will be to world class and a world-class production system.

I'll talk more about these great teachers in Chapter 8, but first, let's look at employee involvement as a necessary first step to world class.

IV.

Building the Foundation—The 757 Airplane Productivity Program

Lesson 4: Employee Involvement Is the Foundation. Without It in Place, You Can't Build a World-Class Production System.

THE QUESTION OF HOW to involve the work force continues to challenge companies worldwide, but is nonetheless an absolutely essential foundation of a world-class operation.

Employee Involvement Begins with Management

In 1982, Ernie Fenn, the vice president and general manager of Boeing's 757 program, asked me how we could make the 757 program into a more participative culture. He wanted to give employees a greater voice in improving how the work got done. I said we needed to change the way management behaved, the way they managed, and that this change had to start and be led at the top if it was to succeed. He asked me how long it would take for me to come up with a process, and I told him I'd be back in three months with an answer.

I did all the research I could do on Japan's management methods, including their application in European and North American companies. My background proved useful for this sort of undertaking. Before starting at Boeing in 1978, I served with the U.S. Army at Headquarters U.S. Army Europe. In my last military assignment, I was responsible for developing human resource training for the army in Europe. I later worked on developing the first training to help pave the way for expanding the role of women in the military. I had soaked up many lessons on the importance of leadership, the ramifications of management behavior, the challenges of cultivating a new culture and "making it happen" in a large organization.

A Model for Employee Involvement

Three months after my conversation with Fenn, I made my appearance with a four-by-six-foot cardboard model I'd put together at home. (I have used this model with a number of variations and improvements since then.) The model became a plan, the plan became a handbook, and the handbook in turn became a process that permeated the 757 program to varying degrees. It eventually traveled with me to Eastern Air Lines for implementation there as well.

I followed up the cardboard model with a memo that contained the following recommendations for getting started. These principles endure.

Enduring Principles

1. Integrate Productivity Improvement/Quality of Work Life (PI/QWL) programs into the normal planning and control systems. PI/QWL must become an attitude, a way of doing things. Don't just tack PI/QWL onto existing systems–it is a long-term investment with potential for significant dollar returns, not a short-term fad.
2. Communicate and reinforce the idea that PI/QWL is not just another program. All efforts must work toward greater productivity by the pervasion of PI/QWL in all plans, methods and systems.
3. Ensure that directors and managers are committed. If you limit productivity thinking and action to middle managers, staff and non-management, the program will lack the long-term support it needs to survive.
4. Don't equate boosting productivity with cutting costs. Increasing productivity will likely decrease costs, but the two are distinct.

5. Consider productivity and "Quality Of Work Life" together. A high QWL is necessary to productivity. It's an upward spiral. Where employees are happy and feel they can influence the outcome, their productivity will rise. When that happens, QWL rises again.

6. Study the many facets of productivity. For example, examine the ratio of output over input not only for labor hours, but also for capital investment, materials and energy.

7. Build training into the program. The workforce must learn what productivity really is, why it is necessary, the units or measurements, how measurement will be performed, incentives, and so on.

8. Look closely at productivity and profitability–the two are distinct but related. If you adopt a productivity program solely for the purpose of raising short-term profits, it may fail. You can increase profits short-term, but perhaps not so with long-term profitability.

9. Continue to design the program to suit the unique needs of the organization. Every organization has its own idiosyncrasies and personality–the trap of following an inspiring case history from another company, division or "sister" corporation/vendor could be your failing.

10. Resist the urge to diffuse the program too quickly. If a pilot program succeeds in manufacturing, for example, it doesn't mean you should do it everywhere–by next week.
11. Set realistic goals. Communicate to the workforce: "There's no free lunch and no overnight success. We must work together as a team."
12. At the appropriate time, bring union management into the act. You don't need an active adversary in-house and the program will work better if everyone pulls together.

Improving productivity from the ground up is a major undertaking at any company. When you're trying to build a new generation of airliner–as the 757 was–it's even more of a challenge. Designing and building a new plane consumes years of deadlines and tight schedules, with little room for delays or errors. The product has to come out on time, within budget and according to specs.

Productivity: Getting Started

Even though high productivity is crucially important for Boeing, we didn't leap headlong into a productivity-improvement program. Vowing to "avoid fishing trips," we instead developed our program slowly, with more painstaking background research. We wanted to make sure that we knew what we wanted, what would work, and only then would we implement it.

We also voiced our agreement that we didn't expect a single technique to get the job done. Far too often companies had relied on only one technique, such as quality circles, with disappointing results.

Given a philosophy heavy on background research and cautious planning, it's not surprising that I had already spent three months just looking into what programs existed elsewhere and how we could adapt them to the 757's needs. Then we spent nine months corralling and taming various ideas into a program that would work for Boeing. Finally, a year after Fenn's memo mandating a program, the 757 employee involvement program shot out of the gates.

Get Management Involved–Or Else

No matter how good the productivity-improvement techniques, they will fail if they aren't backed by an active management. In our case, Ernie Fenn made the first step. The 757 division also made productivity improvement a part of its strategic goals. As additional insurance, department heads organized into an executive council to provide overall direction to the program. Phil Condit, then the Chief Project Engineer, sat on the executive council and was already setting the standard for new management behavior with his active employee rap sessions.

Further down the line, the work of researching productivity programs and adapting them to Boeing's 757 needs fell to action representatives from each department, who were assigned to a productivity steering committee.

A productivity coordinator responsible for the programs within that department assisted each representative on the committee. We thus had a division-wide structure for discussing, selecting and implementing any productivity ideas.

Setting Goals for the Program

We continued our careful, step-by-step approach by developing a clear statement of objectives for the productivity-improvement program as a whole and a strategy for implementing the program. The three objectives were:

- Improve productivity, quality of product and quality of work life.
- Improve output through better employee motivation, involvement, commitment and development.
- Assure that employees have opportunities to identify, solve and control work-related problems.

The strategy stressed a total, coordinated effort, an effort that would affect all methods and systems within the 757 division.

Informed Employees Mean Better Work

Once we completed research, planning and program design, we started to implement our custom-crafted productivity-improvement program.

The first principle was a commitment to inform and involve employees. Each employee received both product and productivity orientation, as well as specific training in ways to solve on-the-job problems.

Significantly, the orientation involved the highest levels of management. In the 757 factory area, for example, workers saw a slide show featuring Ernie Fenn, and heard the factory manager himself explaining what goes into building the airplane and how the employees would take part in our employee-involvement program.

Talking Back to Management

We also valued worker insights. Workers told their stories to management as a part of the productivity steering committee new annual employee survey system.

Why surveys? First, when they are conducted by trained interviewers, as ours were, they provide an excellent way to find out what the work force thinks about productivity and quality in the work place, as well as the quality of work life. Second, the survey became a valuable source of new ideas about improving productivity. However, keep in mind that surveys can shine as a part of a successful program only when management is willing to make the suggested changes.

Division employees were surveyed on nineteen questions in a thirty-minute, one-on-one session with an interviewer. Summaries of the results were reported confidentially to the managers involved.

Some of the survey questions were:

1. How do you know when you have done your job well?

2. What types of activities are you involved in that do not require your level of skill or expertise?

3. What factors, if any, do you believe cause you and others to waste productive time?

4. If any part, or parts, of your job could be made more effective or easier to do, what would they be and how could they be improved?

5. What do you believe motivates people who do the kind of work you do?

The important feature of these surveys was that they were not an attitude survey. Because we were focusing on productivity, we weren't concerned with what employees thought of the parking lot, the cafeteria or the boss. We were, however, vitally interested in determining the factors which kept them from getting the job done.

With the survey completed, we realized that it was time to convince employees that we all share the responsibility for improvement.

Making Suggestions Pay Off

The steering committee expanded the division's employee suggestion program to add more ways for workers to help the productivity-improvement program.

Although our reward for suggestions–up to $10,000–was a powerful incentive, the steering committee found another way to improve the program. No matter what the incentive, the committee discovered in its research, suggestion programs fail when the immediate supervisor is indifferent to them. The problem: supervisors, already heavily burdened with operational requirements, were slow to respond to employee ideas.

We had a simple, yet innovative, solution. Money motivates workers to come up with suggestions. To get supervisors to respond to workers' ideas, we gave them an incentive, too–supervisors shared in the award that employees earned for a suggestion. That gave supervisors a reason to answer their mail and pass suggestions up the ladder to management. With that incentive we worked to respond to suggestions within 10 working days.

Employees were encouraged to do more than talk, however. They were expected to actively take part in finding and implementing solutions to productivity problems.

Productivity Circles

Led by the productivity steering committee, we adopted a program called Productivity Circles, which was very similar to traditional quality circles. But, as usual, we looked very carefully at the idea first.

Many case histories detail quality circle failures that were never advertised. Some of the reasons these programs failed were:

- Companies overemphasized the value of circles in reducing costs.
- Management implemented the circles on a trial-and-error basis.

- Not all managers had been trained to understand and support circles.
- Management's commitment to circles was not evident at the employee level.
- Managers resented the time employees spent in circles.
- Managers felt insecure about letting employees identify problems.
- Managers feared the reaction of unions.
- The circle system was not disciplined and efforts were erratic.

We found that circles succeeded, however, under the following conditions:

- Employees see the system as "theirs" instead of "another management program."
- Employees see effective and timely response to suggestions; that is, real changes in the way things are done.
- Employees feel they are respected members of a company team contributing to the company's productivity goals.
- Management's commitment to circles is uniform at all levels and in all areas.

What Boeing Learned from the 757 Program

The 757 program enjoyed substantial success in cost saving, methods improvement, and improved employee morale. That success results directly from the steps we followed as a team in setting up the program.

The first key step was obtaining top management support for and participation in the program. As we learned from studying other programs, the successes are marked by active management participation, the failures by lack of it.

The second step was careful research and planning. Our research showed that a borrowed program rarely works–it must be tailored to the company's own needs.

The third was commitment to employee training and involvement. No program can be imposed from the top. Employees must understand it and become an active part of it.

Finally, we understood the importance of ongoing effort on productivity improvement. A productivity program is not something that you set up once to solve all the problems: it has to be a continuing commitment.

The first 757 airplane made its maiden flight February 19, 1982–on time, within budget and according to specs. That's what productivity is all about: constructing a good product when it is needed. What made the 757 program different was that we focused on people, not just technology, in meeting our customers' requirements.

My next assignment was to help Eastern Air Lines, at the request of Frank Borman, to get Boeing's program started at Eastern.

V.

Helping an Airline Customer–Lessons Learned From Eastern Airlines

Lesson 5: The Methods, Revolutions and Thresholds That Must Be Crossed to Compete in the Global Market Can Not Be Accomplished from the Bottom Up: They Have to Start from the Top Down.

Little did I know the depths of the swamp and the size of the alligators when I was sent to Eastern's headquarters in Miami in early 1982. The harrowing experiences and lessons of the next year accelerated my learning about organizational change and the power of employee involvement. I also became a steady client of Joe's Stone Crab, the famous Miami restaurant that I frequented with Eastern's management.

I encountered these great learning experiences as a result of my meeting with Paul Johnstone, or "Stoney," as he asked me to call him. Stoney visited Boeing to work on Eastern's purchase of several Boeing 757s. The 757 program impressed him, and when he asked the secret, Boeing executives told him we had a 757 employee participation program. Paul, Eastern's Senior Vice President of Operations Services, had begun an employee participation program at Eastern. He had been convinced that both the company and employees could benefit from their involvement in decisions about how to do their job.

When Stoney returned to Miami, he sent his Manager of Manpower, Bill Croucher, to visit us in Seattle. I presented our 757 productivity program to Croucher. He returned to Miami and sent me a letter requesting more information and assistance. I flew to Miami the end of March, 1982, with my boss, the Manager of Manufacturing Support, and the Director of Manufacturing. We made a presentation about our 757 Employee Participation Program to Stoney and his staff, with Frank Borman, Eastern's Chairman and CEO, attending.

Borman's follow-up was prompt and decisive. The next day he called Eastern's Senior Vice President for Personnel and Corporate Administration and asked him to make 1,000 copies of our 757 employee involvement book, to change the name from Boeing to Eastern, and to adopt the program at Eastern. Next, he called Boeing to ask that the 757 team return to Miami to repeat the presentation for his staff, and that I be loaned to Eastern for six months to help start employee involvement at Eastern. Boeing agreed to both requests.

We went to Miami for the second time and made the same presentation to Borman's entire staff with other managers present from operations. It was a resounding success.

As my bosses dropped me off at the hotel on their way to the airport, I asked, "How long will I be down here? How long is this tour of duty?" They said, "Well, maybe, six or seven weeks." It was going to be a long eight months.

A Tense Environment

The first thing I had to do was to get objective data. I laid out a plan to conduct one-on-one interviews with the top 40 Eastern executives.

The interviews showed that, among other things, labor relations at Eastern were tense, particularly around the issue of the profit-sharing program. It also seemed that while all of the senior managers talked of their support of an employee involvement program, many of them resisted anything more than low-level quality-circles. Furthermore, I learned that Eastern's employees believed that management frequently changed programs but rarely followed through on them.

These findings proved to be my primary challenges during my work at Eastern. I knew the union had to be active in the employee involvement project. I needed to convince managers that it was important, even if it had to be done in an environment of labor friction. Compounding my difficulties, I had to be creative to overcome the determined disinterest of some of the managers, and I needed to encourage a long-term commitment at Eastern to employee involvement.

Another incidental challenge was how to accomplish all of this without getting fired at Boeing for being too aggressive with one of our prime customers. Of course, if I wasn't aggressive enough, the process wouldn't succeed and then both Boeing and Eastern would be unhappy.

I worked out my frustration playing video games at my hotel and meeting at night with my Eastern teammates at Joe's Stone Crab.

Finding the Right People

My office was right next to that of the Senior Vice President of Personnel. He kept a coffee can on his desk, into which his secretary required him to deposit a dollar every time he used overly colorful language.

When I met with him, he told me his ideas for an employee involvement program, including structure and emphasis. I suggested the formation of a planning council to plan how to implement employee involvement. The decisions about how to construct and implement the program should come from the council and not from an Eastern executive. He agreed to this approach and then made a list of the people he thought should be on the council. He also admonished me not to spend any money and not to hire any consultants: "You have no budget."

All the feedback in my interviews told me Eastern was autocratic. In my interviews with senior management and with the leaders in the quality-circle program I developed a better list for the planning council, including only managers noted for their participative style. I went ahead and formed the planning council from my list and informed the Sr. VP of Personnel. He was not pleased, and filled up his coffee can again. I at least knew my "offenses" benefited his local charity.

I held my ground and insisted that many people on his list were too autocratic to make suitable members of an employee involvement council. I also got an agreement from both the planning council members and from Frank Borman to approach the unions about their involvement in the planning of a new employee participation effort. Many planning council members had opposed contacting the unions because of the current labor management tensions.

Amid these challenges, my role was critical, but I also knew I had to quickly work myself out of a job. Eastern would have to steer its own employee involvement effort if it were to become more than just another Eastern program. I drafted and had approved the phasing out of Boeing's involvement, with me assisting only from Seattle in the latter stages of the plan.

Outside Help for Internal Growth

However, Eastern would continue to need outside help. The withdrawal of the IAM from the quality circles program coupled with the growing labor-management tensions suggested the need for an outside consultant who could gain credibility from both the management and the union.

The planning council agreed with me, but the Sr. VP of Personnel did not. He had been specific about not hiring any consultants.

I did anyway. I hired the American Productivity Center, a consulting group that had done some work at Boeing and helped start employee involvement programs at other unionized companies like Ford and Republic Steel. In May 1982 Eastern agreed to a $17,000 contract with APC to help the planning council build a team and educate itself about participative systems. I had them send the bill to the Sr. VP of Personnel, who subsequently called me into his office for an old-fashioned military chewing out. I wondered how long I'd occupy space next door to him.

For several weeks, it was unclear whether Eastern would continue to use the services of the consultants as I felt they should. The Sr. VP was not supporting my position. But I was resolute that this process was going to be owned by Eastern and I wouldn't budge. Eventually I met directly with Borman and got his approval for a longer-term relationship with the consultant group. But even then I knew they needed my help.

As the Harvard Business Case Study on the Eastern Project pointed out, "Boeing as a company had the credibility with Eastern that they needed, and Black–as the designer of the 757 participation program which had so impressed Eastern managers to begin with–had his own influence. The consultants leaned for a while on Black's credibility until they were able to develop sufficient credibility of their own."

As the Harvard case study reports, my second major contribution was persuading the planning council and Eastern's top management to hire outside consultants and to invest generously in the development of employee involvement. I had convincing evidence of the favorable return on investment in employee participation, both in terms of labor-management relations and the balance sheet. Companies have the same overwhelming evidence for the world-class production system. This evidence convinced Borman to invest about $1 million in employee involvement over the next three years.

My third major contribution was in the counseling of patience and long-term commitment as necessary ingredients to a successful employee involvement program.

What I Learned at Eastern

1. If you need consultants, pick the right ones. They must be focused on enabling people and not on promoting technology.
2. If you are going to help managers change, then you yourself must change first. Work with, not against, management in doing it.
3. Getting managers and non-managers focused on the production system or the "system of work" is paramount. If you cannot achieve this focus, your program can easily become just one more initiative in a long list of initiatives.
4. If the Kaizen philosophy of continuous improvement is not the primary focus of management behavior and energy, your efforts and those of the company will probably fail.

As 1984 came to a close, Frank Borman sent me a letter thanking me for my help in successfully instituting an employee involvement program at Eastern. His congratulations signified the conclusion of an especially challenging personal lesson for me on organizational behavior. This experience gave me the tools to put the infrastructure in place for future successful top down implementations.

Back in Seattle, I faced an even tougher challenge than Eastern. My next assignment was to move into the narrow body factory (727/737/757) and implement what I'd learned on the 757 Program and at Eastern Air Lines.

VI.

Promoting the Process— The Power of the Promotion Office

Lesson 6: The Goal of a World-Class Production System Can Only Be Achieved with a JIT Promotion Office to Help Promote the Process.

Becoming a world-class producer requires focus and tenacity, passion and commitment. It also requires promotion from the top down in order to succeed. Companies around the world have found that efforts to improve cannot be allowed to become a sideline activity. Boeing began to formally implement an infrastructure to support continuous improvement with a movement called Quality Improvement Centers. I led the formation of our first two centers, and later helped launch the first Seattle Boeing JIT Promotion Office. We started building this infrastructure for continuous improvement in Boeing Aerospace in 1984 with a Steering Committee made up of senior managers. They met for months to support efforts such as quality circles, supplier improvement, long-range productivity activities, recognition and motivation.

Together these senior managers ensured that quality improvement remained a top priority in all departments year to year (see Figure 7).

Quality Training Starting at the Top

We initiated sessions for senior management through a comprehensive training program set up by the Quality Improvement Center. In the fall of 1984, Boeing Aerospace Company (BAC) President H. K. Hebeler, BAC vice presidents and other senior executives attended a seminar in quality improvement conducted by Dr. Alvin Gunneson.

In the spring of 1985, these senior managers attended the Upper Management and Quality Training session, conducted by international quality improvement expert J. M. Juran.

Quality Councils: An Infrastructure

In addition to the senior manager committee on the aerospace side, we established 13 quality councils to structure improvement throughout aerospace. Then we put 18 management improvement teams at work within BAC to improve quality.

The quality councils implemented quality improvement primarily through management improvement teams, quality circles and statistical management. Statistical management using statistical techniques to isolate problem areas and determine appropriate solutions was introduced, a first in the company. Other quality improvement activities included engineering productivity and supplier improvement.

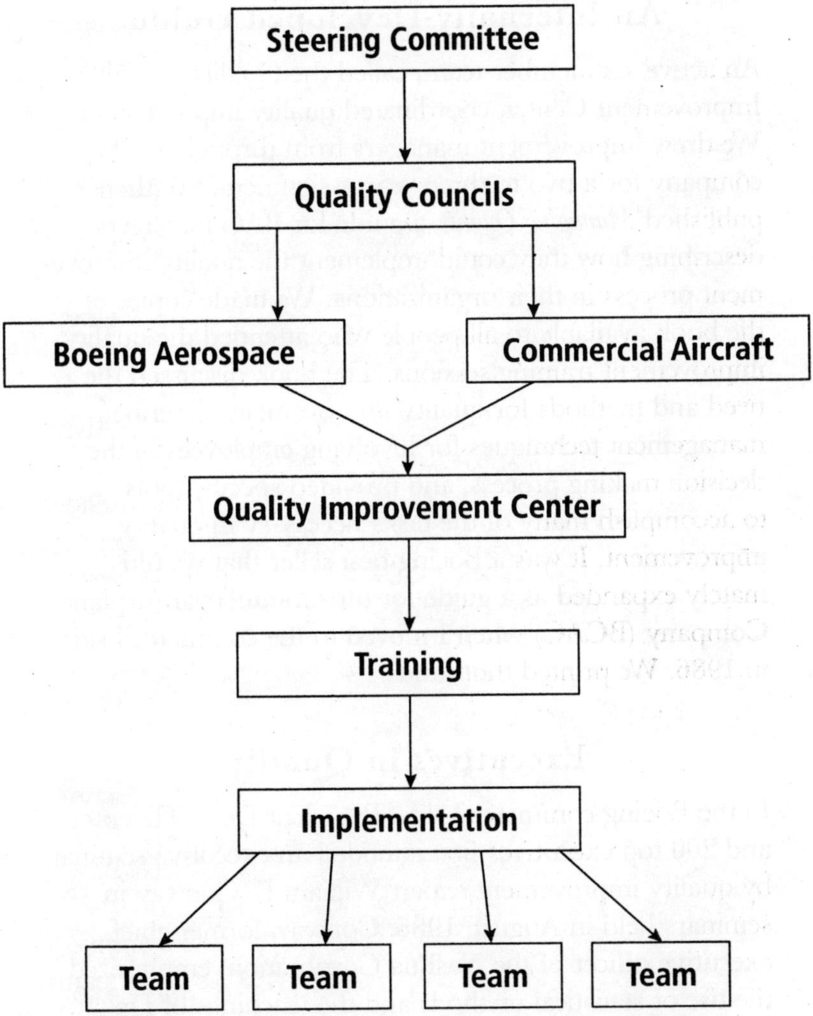

Figure 7. Beginnings of a world-class infrastructure

An Internally-Developed Guide

An active six-member team, called the Quality Improvement Center, coordinated quality improvement. We drew improvement managers from throughout the company for a two to three year assignment. We then published *Managing Quality,* a guide for BAC managers describing how they could implement the quality improvement process in their organizations. We made copies of the book available to all people who attended the quality improvement training sessions. The book discussed the need and methods for quality improvement, described management techniques for involving employees in the decision-making process, and provided specific tools to accomplish many of the tasks necessary in quality improvement. It was a Boeing best-seller that we ultimately expanded as a guide for the Commercial Airplane Company (BCAC) when I moved to the commercial side in 1986. We printed thousands.

Executives in Quality

In the Boeing commercial side, President Dean Thornton and 200 top executives first attended an executive seminar by quality improvement expert William E. Conway in seminars held in August, 1986. Conway, former chief executive officer of the Nashua Corporation, emphasized the use of statistical methods and the teachings of Dr. Edward Deming. Conway periodically came to Boeing to conduct seminars. Our goal in offering this education was to have every manager focused on eliminating waste . . . the waste of labor, capital, materials and energy.

The Conway seminars were only the beginning of the rapidly expanding BCAC quality improvement effort that eventually included all of Boeing. We initiated a two-day Managing Quality seminar. Starting with upper management and working down, the seminar was presented to all BCAC supervisors, managers and executives prior to 1988. We wanted our managers to gain an understanding of the need for quality improvement and to start leading the process.

This seminar was developed by our Quality Improvement Center, an early version of what we hoped would eventually function in the same way as Toyota's Kaizen Promotion Office. Established at the outset of the BCAC Quality Improvement Plan, the Quality Improvement Center's mission was to assist and support BCAC management in the continuous improvement of quality and productivity.

Center activities and responsibilities included:

1. Reviewing division program and organization improvement plans; providing consultation
2. Serving as the focal point for the planning and coordination of quality improvement education and training activities
3. Conducting research and study of industry and business practices and trends; making information available to company management
4. Supporting the BCAC Steering Committee and Quality Council
5. Maintaining an extensive library and resource center of educational and training materials

The center's professional staff was responsible for:

1. Research and study
2. The library and resources
3. Introductory and awareness training (we designed and implemented the initial core for all BCAC Quality Improvement classes and seminars), consultation, support and assistance to company organizations

We chose functional representatives from all over BCAC and assigned them to the center on a 12-month, rotating basis. They were thoroughly educated in quality improvement concepts and were trained in improvement tools and methods. The representatives worked with their respective organizations on implementing quality improvement plans and projects, and provided a broad base of experience and resources to assist problem solving in all other organizations.

Seminars

Interspersed among the presentations by top executives from BCAC and highly respected companies around the country were "breakouts," where small teams form to discuss seminar topics, brainstorm, develop plans, define problems and generate solutions. One particularly enjoyable and enlightening breakout was an exercise called Desert Survival, which compared individual strategy with team consensus and consumed the first afternoon. An industry example occupied most of the second afternoon.

Executives from Caterpillar, John Fluke, Xerox, IBM, Honeywell, General Dynamics, ALCOA, Ford, Hewlett-Packard and Precision Cast Parts made presentations. These companies were well into the quality improvement process. The speakers took part in our discussions, donating their time to pass along experience and answer questions.

Response to these seminars assured us we were on the right track, but we knew that to be complacent was to stagnate. We developed other seminars. A nine-day Train the Trainer course designed to provide key people with the basics for implementing quality improvement through team effort was followed by Facilitator Training, Team Leader Training and Team Member Training, all aimed at making the improvement process more efficient and successful. We implemented specialized courses including Process Control Methods and Design of Experiments. These educational roles in themselves were a full-time job for the Quality Improvement Center.

The Power of Learn/Do

The next transition beyond traditional quality improvement must be a change in paradigms. The paradigm change is away from classroom, seminars and teaching in the traditional sense. It is incorporating the power of what you hear and what you see into action, into doing–the power of learn/do–not waiting for the perfect plan.

This is the power of JIT/Lean Thinking. This is the power of Kaizen. This is the power that our bright young leaders of corporations, government, and service must quickly learn and unleash in North America and the world. It is a mandate for the future economic health of our economies.

There is no cookbook for implementing the world-class production system of Taiichi Ohno. On his deathbed, Mr. Ohno's last words were reported to be, "No kanban." It is very likely that he meant the ultimate target is synchronous flow, delivery by the supplier just-in-time, just at the moment needed, arriving like a Japanese bullet train.

It is an experiential process requiring a passion to strive for perfection, the precise design of which is not contained in this or any other publication I know of. To get started, however, both Ohno and his student Yoshiki Iwata require the formation of the JIT Promotion Office.

The JIT Promotion Office

Just In Time is an operating philosophy and strategy: the beating heart of the world-class production system. It is all-encompassing, requiring total management commitment from the top down. One of the key jobs of the Toyota promotion office is to get rid of competing and conflicting approaches (such as Total Quality Management) because JIT incorporates them all. JIT's main tool is continuous improvement and it incorporates other TQM tools such as Hoshin Kanri (Policy Deployment), Daily Management, Process Management, etc.

Another job of the promotion office is to maintain the pressure and not allow anyone to opt out of the process.

The promotion office at places like Toyota is staffed only with line managers on a not more than thirty-six-month assignment to help lead, promote, train and accelerate Kaizen (continuous improvement) and Kaikaku (revolutionary change). This means people from the office and factory with credibility, experience, commitment, passion and guts to stand up to managers who are roadblocks. Promotion office members must know how to work with sensei, the master teachers that you will bring in to your company to help you pursue perfection through evolution (Kaizen) and revolution (Kaikaku).

What is the size of this force for rapid change? The size of the promotion office should be 1 percent of your total organization head count adjusted by level. If you have 5,000 employees, 50 should be engaged full-time out of the promotion office. Another 5 percent (who do not report to the promotion office) should be dispersed throughout the company, working full time in support of overnight Kaizen. This includes maintenance, tooling, and carpentry employees who build simple tools, shadow boards, and other items for the support of rapid improvement.

A company with 100,000 employees should have at least 50 line managers working throughout the organization from the promotion office. They must report to a senior executive who has responsibility and authority for the majority of the organization. Ideally, it should be the president. The chain of command from the promotion office to the president should be no more than one level.

The promotion office should not spend hundreds of

hours and dollars on strategy. The strategy is done. It is in Chapter 9 and comes from Toyota's success. It is also contained in the books of Womack and Jones and in the work of industry leaders such as Art Byrne of Wiremold and many others. The strategy is also the working strategy of Shingijutsu.

The promotion office should not become a strategic planning office because the planning has been done . . . and it works . . . and it is simple. Promotion office members and their executive leaders have a simple objective: Get lean, get lean, get lean.

VII.

Japan Study Missions—The Power of Learning and Doing

Lesson 7: If You're Not Simple, You Can't Be Fast, and If You Aren't Fast, You Can't Win.

Going to Japan to see world class and then *doing* Kaizen will help you understand the power of simplicity. The more I learned about world class and faced the challenges of introducing change, the more it began to disturb me that in many of our speeches in and outside the company we talked about being world class without really knowing what it meant. We all thought we were world class because we had the majority of the market share and were number one in aerospace in the world. Why would we not be world class?

I began to realize that we would never break through all the operational paradigms facing us unless we really studied and internalized world class performance, regardless of the industry. Our leaders needed to study world class, see it, talk about, believe it, then lead it and do it on the job at Boeing.

In the end, that is precisely what happened. The process began in 1984 when I reported to Bill Selby in the Boeing Aerospace Company. I had arranged for Norman Bodek, the North American Japan Study Mission pioneer, to come in and brief about 40 of our top operations executives about what the Japanese were doing in creating a world-class production system. The briefing went well, but the opinion of most everyone was, "Why should we go to Japan? We are already "world class.""

Then, when assigned to the Boeing Commercial Airplane Company (BCAC), I met and learned from Colin Fox, Managing Director of Deltapoint, a local consulting firm based in Bellevue, Washington. He told me about taking company executives to study in Japan, a process he learned from Norman Bodek. I told him our executives needed to go to Japan because they thought Boeing was already world class. I convinced Bruce Gissing, our Senior VP of Operations, and got the first mission launched in 1990.

Across the Ocean in Search of a Vision

Bruce Gissing, Senior Vice President of Operations, led the first team. I was included, along with the Director of International Business Operations for the New Airplane Division; the Vice President of Operations Development; the Vice President/General Manager of Fabrication Division; the Senior Manager of International Business; and the Vice President of Engineering.

When we came back, we recommended that the missions continue. It was my job to help facilitate and promote our findings and learnings. Gissing's team met every Monday at 6:00 A.M. for a year.

More missions followed as a result of our successful efforts and Gissing's leadership. The missions became part of the continuing effort within Boeing to learn how to improve the quality of products and services, business and management practices, productivity and profit, design, development and manufacturing capabilities. All the missions had the following goals:

Mission Goals

1. Learn first-hand the strategies and practices of world-class Japanese manufacturing companies.
2. Use the knowledge gained about those companies to evaluate and benchmark Boeing's current and planned approaches and strategies.
3. Develop recommendations from the benchmarking analysis.
4. Most importantly, identify the management principles and practices that made them world class and then adapt them to our business.

Choosing an Expedition Team

Success of the mission depended on selection and preparation of the teams. We selected and carefully prepared participants as though for the mountaineering expedition it would prove to be. They had to meet rigid criteria.

The President of BCAC, Dean Thornton, went to Japan with the second team, while the third team included Frank Shrontz, then Chairman and CEO, and Phil Condit, the present Chairman. A total of 95 executives participated on seven successive teams over nearly two years.

Preparing the Teams

Mission preparation was arduous for everyone. It included 45 hours of classroom education about world-class manufacturing concepts. Each team member was required to read a substantial amount of material, including five books. Companies we visited were world class, and most were Deming Prize winners. Two of the companies were Japan Quality Control Prize winners. All of the companies our teams visited demonstrated superior manufacturing capabilities, employing four essential systems: Total Quality Control (TQC), Total Employee Involvement, Just In Time Manufacturing, and Total Productive Maintenance (TPM). Finally, the companies chosen were considered crucial to understanding Japan's competitive strength and capabilities.

The actual trip portion of the missions lasted fourteen to sixteen days with preparatory work starting three months before departure. I kept an attendance log on everyone and showed it at the start of each preparatory session. It worked. Everyone, led by Frank Shrontz and Phil Condit, had perfect attendance.

They were great students. The days in Japan were full and intense, balancing study and review of relevant material with factory visits. Each day started very early, and the day's activities continued into evening. Participants were required to use a standard form, still used today on our current Japan trips, to record and share observations in order to promote learnings as they traveled by bus back to the hotel.

Learning in Japan

At a mid-trip review meeting we shared observations, impressions and new understandings. Everyone took a final written examination in Tokyo at the end of the trip. The exam covered relevant theory emphasized during the factory visits and exchanges with Japanese mangers. The trip concluded with an extensive debriefing in Japan. I conducted a post-trip evaluation immediately following the return of the teams from Japan, collecting detailed responses from team members about what they learned and what they were doing differently as a result of the trip. I also created a management visibility room with the results posted and updated on the wall.

After collecting many recommendations and action items, Gissing was assigned to lead the implementation of the Japan study mission learnings. We spent one year creating a four-day course called "Managing for World-Class Competitiveness." We designed it to communicate what we learned in Japan and how we could make it work for the Boeing Company. The course was taught to more than 100,000 employees by our managers.

What We Learned

We are still implementing what we learned, now in the form of the Boeing Production System. Here are some of the important lessons we learned in Japan.

1. URGENCY: Management is responsible for making a company world class.
2. CUSTOMER FOCUS: Customers are the most important consideration in everything you do.
3. QUALITY: You must develop unprecedented expectations about quality.
4. PEOPLE: People are strategically important to a company's competitiveness.
5. PRODUCTION SYSTEMS: World-class production philosophies and methods represent a fundamental shift in thinking, and a revolution for achieving improvements in quality, cost, delivery and flexibility. Central to achieving world-class production systems are designing and building quality in, adding value and eliminating waste.
6. MANAGEMENT SYSTEMS: These systems must support the capability of people to produce superior results. The three-part management system consists of Management By Policy, Daily Management and Cross-Functional Management.

7. IMPLEMENTATION: If you want to, you will make it all happen.

The next question was determining the cast for our change to world-class production. Who could we employ to help us to world class?

VIII.

Champions, Consultants, Sensei—The Difference and Their Key Roles

Lesson 8: Hiring Consultants to Come to Your Company, Collect Data, and Feed It Back to You with a Strategy That Requires You to Spend Money, Add People and Buy Expensive Machines and Equipment Means One Thing . . . You Are Really Stupid.

CHAMPIONS ARE THE INTERNAL LEADERS needed to make the world-class production system a reality. Champions are vital to an evolving system because they know how to make new paths for others to follow.

Champions lead. Champions build leaders. Champions vigorously promote the process, and they lead by doing. They lead by practicing Kaizen, continuous improvement (see Figure 8). At Boeing we have been fortunate to have many champions. They often voice their conviction that people are the building blocks of a world-class production system. They lead by walking the talk.

The champion's role is best summed up by Art Byrne, CEO of Wiremold, who is one of industry's strongest champions.

1. Get out in front, hands on, don't delegate
2. Take lots of leaps of faith
3. Set stretch goals
4. Create an environment where it is okay to fail
5. Provide air cover for those embattled in the trenches

Once the champion is moving the process in the right direction, you can bring in consultants from the outside if you think it is necessary.

Consultants: Use Them Wisely

Used wisely, consultants can help you build the infra-structure, the framework upon which you build the system, one step at a time.

Consultants must be managed, focused and supportive. Some consultants carry laptops, conduct big expensive studies, then make complicated colored overhead presentations and submit a bill before they've even started. These are not the consultants I am recommending for this purpose.

If you use consultants without deliberate planning and thought, you'll never be able to hammer together a world-class production system. What may emerge in its place is a push, MRP II, complex system focusing on creating waste rather than eliminating it.

Such attempts at mirroring a world-class production system will likely hinge on computers on the factory floor storing inaccurate data reflecting yesterday's status. It will be an expensive system. It will be a system you'll one day dismantle.

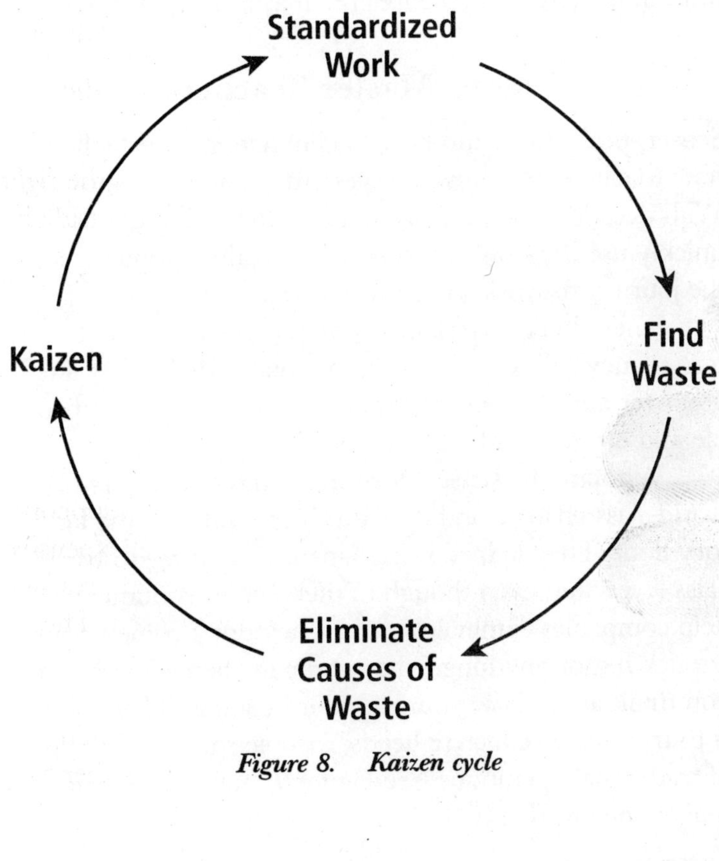

Figure 8. ***Kaizen cycle***

As a world-class system thrives, the supervisors and the managers who make kaizen a way of life eventually take over the internal consultant's role. This is a long journey which must be embarked upon. It's not a short haul to get to this point.

Art Byrne, Wiremold CEO, has been at it since 1991. He requires every manager to spend as long as a year in the promotion office leading Kaizen. The manager then goes back to the line organization knowing the JIT tools intimately and practices them as a way of life forever.

Sensei: Master Teachers

Sensei speak waste and how to eliminate it. They tell you how to eliminate it now, not yesterday and not tomorrow. With decades of experience at their disposal, they can quickly use their own wisdom and creativity to jump-start the journey to world-class production.

They don't carry laptop computers. They don't make fancy-colored overhead presentations. They will tell you over and over again: "Spend no money, add no people and create no additional space."

Who are the sensei? Sensei are master teachers of world-class change, and they produce results on the factory floor. They helped bring Japanese industry to world-class levels and even though in their sixties continue to help companies eliminate waste. They don't come with a quick fix for anything. They come to change the way you think about how you run your business. Their goal is to transform "concrete heads," people stuck in the rut of traditional operations (see Figure 9), into people with minds open to Kaizen.

Figure 9. No concrete heads

I believe that the best sensei to assist you in implementing the Toyota production system are those of Shingijutsu Ltd., the firm headed by Yoshiki Iwata and Chihiro Nakao (see Chapter 3). With their help, companies all over the world–including Porsche, General Electric, Hitachi, Benz Brazil, Wiremold, Danaher, and Hon Industries–have reported major, bottom-line improvements in a thirty-six-month period.

Shingijutsu was founded by Yoshiki Iwata, Chihiro Nakao and Akira Takenaka in 1987. They were protégés of Taiichi Ohno, father of the Toyota production system. They are determined that the knowledge they developed in implementing the Toyota production system will contribute to the productivity improvement of other companies and to society.

They will only consult with companies that have a strong commitment by top management to install a world-class production system, nothing less. They consult shop-floor Kaizen. They visit your factory floor, analyze quickly how you build your product, and immediately start Kaizen to change the factory.

Sensei have a vision of perfection, and it is the total elimination of waste achieved through Kaizen and Kaikaku. They prescribe a winning formula:

1. Proactive leadership
2. Time-based strategy (Cycle time, Takt Time, Lead Time)
3. Kaizen breakthrough methodology

They will start you on the long road to perfection, and it will be easier than you think.

IX.

The Roadmap—Striving for Perfection Through Kaizen

Lesson 9: In Measuring Progress Toward the Vision, Metrics Must Be Few, Simple, Meaningful and Directly Linked to Visual Targets in the Workplace.

BEFORE YOU START DOWN THE ROAD to world-class production, you need to have some high expectations because you get what you aim for. Art Byrne, CEO of Wiremold, will tell you that if you're not achieving the following targets then you don't understand how to run a world-class business:

1. Free up 50 percent of floor space
2. Double inventory turns in two years; quadruple turns in four
3. Improve productivity 15 to 25 percent per year
4. Cut lead times from weeks to days
5. Achieve major quality improvements (10X)

In order to achieve these targets, remember the powerful role of people in this system.

People undertake tremendous responsibilities in the world-class production system, but their jobs also become more rewarding. They have more freedom to influence their work and make necessary changes. Both in the factory and in the office, people develop standardized work procedures for their own jobs. They strive continuously to find ways to improve those procedures through Kaizen. Working as a team, they use kanban to manage the flow of work and to order parts and materials. Together they work to master every job so that any team member can help or even fill in for any other member of the team. It is truly a team effort.

A Flexible and Responsive Workforce

For those accustomed to the regimented structure of traditional production, the world-class production system and the broad-ranging responsibilities that it assigns to people doing the work can come as a shock. Traditional systems depend on complex, rigid job descriptions. The world-class production system does not. It cultivates people who are flexible in acquiring multiple skills. Traditional systems pad the schedule for many tasks with so-called reserve time. The world-class system leaves no time in the work cycle for any task that is not absolutely necessary to produce value for the customer. The system empowers the people who do the work to stop the production line whenever they detect a problem, and demands management to take action on the problem immediately. The focus is on fixing the process, not on blame.

Responsibility and authority are motivational, while nothing is more demoralizing than being unproductive. Experience proves that the more authority people have to manage their own work, the more inclined they are to pursue improvements in that work. People who can translate their own ideas into visible improvements in production flow and product quality take pride in their work, in their jobs and in their companies. It is that simple. This applies to engineering and other white-collar functions as well.

The world-class production system enforces a creative tension in the workplace. People don't coast. People want to do a good job.

Just In Time production demands continuous focus. Continuous improvements in the name of Kaizen demand dedicated efforts to find better ways of doing things. Management must do its part in structuring a workplace environment that supports and nurtures the initiative of people. The overall result is a stimulating workplace where people take responsibility for their own destinies.

A Single Goal: No Waste

Everyone focuses on the total elimination of waste. The result: people are only engaged in work that adds value. Everyone works to achieve one piece flow in the factory or in the office; one piece flow of product or one piece flow of design, it doesn't matter. The objective is the same: evolve from batch production (push scheduling) to flow production (pull forecasting and scheduling without complex MRP).

World-Class Production System

Consistent and simple measures reveal the organization's progress towards world-class production (see Figure 10). Here are eleven principles to follow in creating a world-class production system.

Eleven Principles To Follow

1. Throw out your old attitudes. Think of ways to make the new ideas work.
2. Don't say we can't, you can't or they can't. Say we can.
3. Don't accept excuses and don't require perfection. Remember that 50 percent is OK.
4. Quick and crude is better than slow and elegant.
5. Don't substitute money for brains. No concrete heads!
6. Correct problems immediately.
7. Don't be afraid to ask why five times to find the root cause.
8. When generating ideas for improvement, never settle for the first one you come up with. Choose the best idea of at least seven.

What is Measured	Targets
Andon	Prediction of abnormalities
Communication	Open, two way, cross-functional, timely
Flow Production	One piece, operators can run and set up all equipment in cell
Jidoka	System in place to stop at any abnormalities
Layout Techniques	Possible to change layout daily
Lot Sizes	Set up<100sec, Lot Size=1 piece
Management	Lead Kaizen daily, focused on removing waste and not fixing blame . . . create a learning culture . . . barrier removers and enablers . . .
Organizational Structure	Flat, decentralized, engineering and manufacturing teaming
Pacemaker	Stop at designated locations
Pull Production, Level Schedule	All repetitive production is pulled
People	Practice Kaizen daily, work to takt time, secure, responsible, diverse, respectful of others and free to take risks
Production Planning and Control	Decentralized and simple, MRP planning . . . JIT execution, kanban in full implementation, Kaizen by all workers trained in industrial engineering methods
Quality Assurance	>95% key processes are capable, <10 PPM defective rate
Recognition, Reward	Meaningful, timely, continuous, consistent
Safety	Zero accidents, integrated safety system in place
Standard Operations	In place everywhere . . . working to takt time, standard work in process, standard work visible
Teams	Set goals, know the work, use data, do Kaizen everyday, work to takt time
Training	Just In Time, LearnDo, PlanDo, learning shared across organization
TPM Maintenance	Equipment Efficiency>95%, Autonomous maintenance by operators
Suppliers	In a long-term partnership with the customer practicing all the world-class production system measures and targets
Visual Control	Whole floor is visible, can take status by walking around
5S	Discipline of standard operations

Figure 10. Target and measures for world class

9. Improvement is made at the workplace, not from the office.
10. Ideas from more people is better, especially if the people are closer to the problem.
11. There are no limits to improvement, only limits you set for yourself.

Following these principles, these fifteen steps can create a world-class production system.

Fifteen Steps to World-Class Production

1. Develop a sense of urgency to get lean–one half less of everything. Introduce this strategy.
2. Identify an outside sensei, a master to help you learn how to eliminate waste.
3. Establish a promotion office and develop internal leaders with a passion for continuous improvement. Have them teach and "spark fires" using simple "lean fever" training materials they have developed.
4. Precisely define value for your business in terms of specific products with specific capabilities offered at specific prices through a dialogue with specific customers. Anything else is MUDA (waste).
5. Get rid of competing strategies (TQM, process management, etc.) They are all part of world class.

6. Implement the waste elimination strategy:
   - Workplace Kaizen to eliminate waste in how the work is done
   - Equipment Kaizen to improve equipment reliability
   - Kaikaku (innovation) to powerfully reconfigure the value stream
7. Get rid of the waste using Kaizen. The promotion office oversees Kaizen. This study team approach, comprised of cross-functional hourly and salaried workers, should get the facts and set objectives and take only five days to do it. It is rapid, quick, accelerated change using JIT tools and can be done in both the office and the factory.
8. Make value, not waste, flow.
9. Turn the organization on its side in order to create a clear path from suppliers, through the work processes of the company, to customers. When flow is introduced, products requiring years to design are done in months. Orders taking days to process are completed in hours. The weeks or months of throughput time for conventional physical production are reduced to minutes or days. Manage horizontally across the value chain.
10. Focus on cutting lead time, cycle time, and working to customer requirements by meeting takt time. Takt time is the heartbeat, it is the

meter of customer requirements. If you produce to takt time, you are making the product at the rate you can sell.

11. Manage by policy rather than by objectives, through Hoshin Kanri (policy deployment).
12. Get old-style managers who refuse to change out of the way, and recognize those whose embrace or championship of world-class principles can change others.
13. Continually strive to reach perfection following the ground rules of Kaizen: spend no money, add no people and create no additional space.
14. Start bringing your suppliers and customers into the process, building lasting relationships that ultimately will create a seamless enterprise.
15. Start helping your customers make these same changes.

Results

World-class production systems are a formidable challenge, but the rewards can be nothing less than the survival and success of a company.

Time-based competition has caused truly remarkable changes on the factory floor. By applying Lean/JIT principles and tools and "just doing it," typical improvements tend to defy belief: cycle time reduced by 20 to 90 percent, defects reduced up to 100 percent, non-value-added tasks reduced 20 to 80 percent. In some North American companies, 60 to 70 percent of the product's cycle time is now value-added activity. That statistic was unheard of a decade ago.

Chihiro Nakao, President of Shingijutsu, has been working with Porsche for almost three years. The new 911 has gone from drawing board to pre-production in less than thirty-six months. This is a record for Porsche, which embraced time-based Kaizen and JIT practices to slash costs and speed development.

The advantages of the world-class production system, however, are not limited to the manufacturing environment. In the next chapter, we'll examine waste elimination in services and in the health care factory.

X.

Beyond Manufacturing–The Office and Service Industry Wasteland

Lesson 10: The Greatest Opportunities to Eliminate Waste Are in the Corporate "Waste"land: the Office, the Engineering Floors, Factories and the Service Industry.

My experience working with organizations trying to get lean is that the "beef" is in the office or service sectors, but this is also where the "concrete heads" prevail. Speed on the factory floor is not enough, particularly when factory costs may be only 7 to 12 percent of total costs.

A good example is the health care costs in an average hospital. One hospital conducted a three-year audit of its labor expenses (see Figure 11). Only 16 percent of its costs had anything to do with patient care delivery. The rest are all typical overhead and mostly non-value-added costs that customers are unwilling to pay for but for which they keep getting charged.

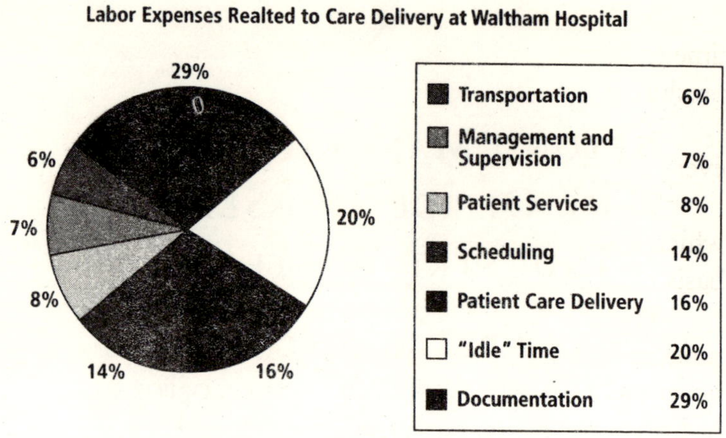

Figure 11. Patient care expenses as percentage of total cost at a hospital [2]

Customers are unimpressed by short manufacturing lead teams (start to finish) if the other parts of the delivery chain make response time slow. Time consumed anywhere in the value chain is equally valuable. It follows, then, that time squeezed from any part of the chain has the same value to customers. To be a true time-based competitor, a business must tackle the entire chain by reducing waste in activities outside of the "factory" walls–these are the activities of the "white-collar factory."

Watching the Clock

I keep addressing time. There are three basic times a company must target on the way to becoming world class.

First, you must reduce lead time–the total time between customer order and delivery of the product.

Second, you must reduce cycle time–the amount of time to accomplish the standard work sequence for one product, excluding queue time.

Third, you must work to takt–the time frame for every item to be produced that day.

To improve these times, you establish standard work, which is the tasks and sequence of those tasks. This is the basis of improvement in the Toyota production system.

Without emphasis on these three times, and continuous improvement through the power of Kaizen, you'll never get to be world class whether you operate a factory or hospital or hamburger joint.

Introduce Kaizen into the White-Collar Environment

I have said that some U.S. factory operations have achieved unprecedented reductions in lead time, boosting value-added activity and dramatically cutting costs. Yet, direct labor is less than 5 percent of the product costs, because white-collar activities in these same organizations continue to represent an increasing percentage of costs.

But reducing waste in white-collar activities has generally taken a back seat by management. The more "macho" reengineering, technology-focused activities have reorganized many white-collar organizations, but the waste in the processes has remained and even increased. Kaizen has not been prevalent and the tools and techniques of JIT have not been applied as they should be to achieve similar quantum reductions and improvements in the bottom line.

It has been my experience that management would rather do "one-time" reengineering than get engaged in the hands-on, long-term commitment of Kaizen and Kaikaku.

Where Is the Value Added?

The percentage of time devoted to value-added activity in white-collar processes is typically less than 5 percent. This means that about 95 percent of activity is non-value-added. These processes are still managed by the methods of traditional batch manufacturing. White-collar processes still resemble the North American factories of the 1950s and 1960s, a tragic statement in terms of management's failure to take advantage of great opportunities to improve the bottom line.

White-collar processes can benefit from Kaizen and JIT. As Joe Blackburn states in his timeless 1992 article "Time-Based Competition: White-Collar Activities,[3]" "The JIT mode is appealing for several reasons. First, the basic objectives of JIT–eliminating waste in the organization, simplicity, total quality and speed–are desirable attributes for all the firm's processes. Second, the JIT model promotes organizational learning: knowledge attained through JIT implementation is recyclable for use throughout the firm. Third, JIT embodies the principle of Kaizen, or incremental, but continuous, improvement. Firms that adopt the philosophy of Kaizen tend to attack new product development in small, manageable chunks–singles, instead of home runs."

Chihiro Nakao often admonished his students in Kaizen not to wait to get into the pro game until they have a 100 percent chance of hitting a home run, but rather to learn to bunt consistently. Indeed, victories in baseball and Kaizen alike hinge not on home runs, but on filling the bases.

Health Care: Sick with Waste

Health care is an excellent example to demonstrate the potential for improvement in a white-collar environment. The Shingijutsu consultants liken a factory floor mechanic, who needs all of his tools and supplies with him at all times, to a surgeon needing the scalpel handed to him by the nurse. "How would you feel if you were on the operating table and the surgeon had to run to another corner of the hospital to get a needle to sew you up?" they often query. Curiously, the health care industry does not yet apply that basic operating room efficiency concept in the rest of their undertakings. The challenges for the health care industry are the inefficiencies of traditional hospital structure, and we've all experienced these.

Patients and staff travel long distances in the hospital, encountering many delays. In one study, this in-hospital travel was 130,000 miles per year not counting nursing travel (see Figure 12).

In five to six days, hospital employees caring for stroke patients made 60 round trips, traveling eight miles. They spent countless hours processing and distributing paperwork. Indicative of all of this waste is the fact that

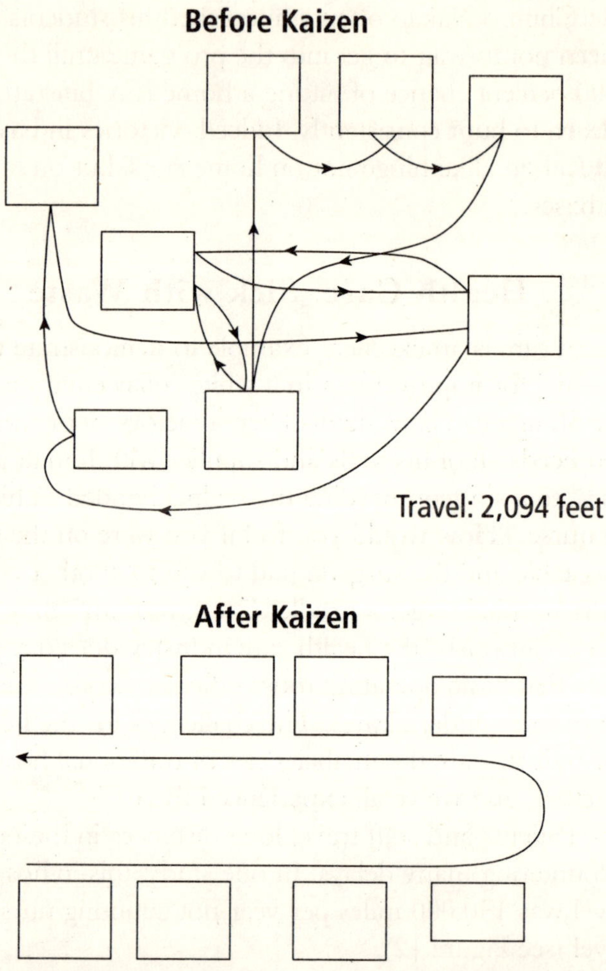

Figure 12. Travel distance for sterile processing cart before and after Kaizen

usually no one person is fully aware of all aspects of the patient's status.

Eighty percent of the time required to provide services results from the traditional centralized structure. In health care, non-value-added time is defined as time spent on efforts that do not directly contribute to achieving patient outcomes and/or meeting patient needs (see Figures 13a and b).

Other examples of waste in health care are[4]:

- Nurses spend about 50 percent of their time on "non-professional" tasks
- Personnel spend about 20 percent of their time "idle"–ready but waiting; 29 percent on documentation; 6 percent on travel and patient transportation; and 14 percent scheduling and coordinating.
- Ancillary Specialists spend 40 percent of their time traveling
- Of $130.5 billion spent annually on labor expense for U.S.hospitals, $99.2 billion pays for non-value-added activities

Kaizen: A Tool for the Journey to World Class

When you apply the JIT tools and techniques plus the power of Kaizen in the white-collar world, you eliminate waste as you standardize the work. It simply means that whether in an office, in engineering, or in a hospital

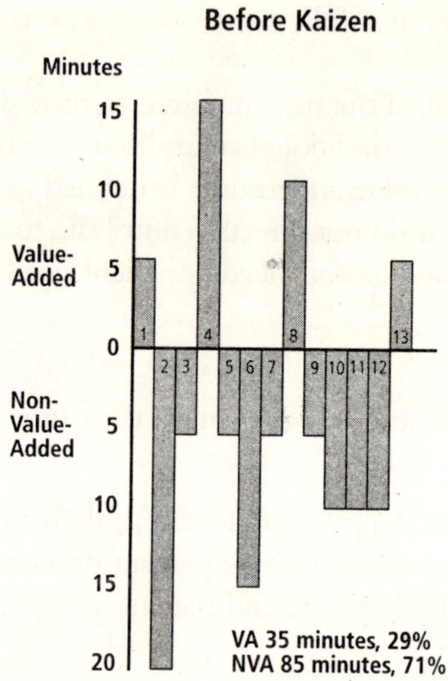

1. Patient arrives and signs in
2. Patient waits 20 minutes
3. Nurse 1 takes patient to ultra-sound room
4. Dr. performs ultra-sound. Gives patient instruction to have HCG shot at noon
5. Patient goes back to waiting room
6. Patient waits 15 minutes
7. Nurse 3 takes patient to blood station
8. Patient has blood drawn
9. Nurse 3 takes patient to exam room
10. Patient waits 10 minutes
11. Nurse verifies HCG to be given at 9PM. Patient says Doctor said noon. Nurse says 9PM is protocol but she is not sure. Patient asks nurse to call Doctor.
12. Nurse calls Doctor. He is confused about process. Agrees HCG to be given at 9PM.
13. Nurse gives patient HCG to be self-injected at 9PM.

Figure 13a. Process for receiving ultrasound before Kaizen

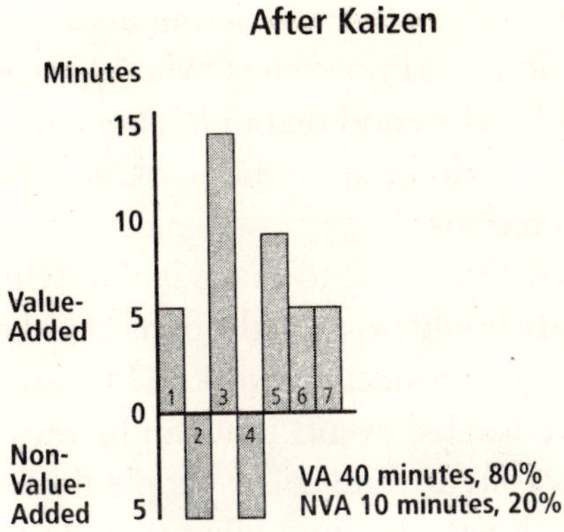

1. Patient arrives and signs in
2. Nurse 1 takes patient to ultra-sound room
3. Doctor performs ultra-sound
4. Nurse 3 takes patient to blood station
5. Patient has blood drawn
6. Nurse 2 gives patient HCG to be self-injected at 9PM
7. Patient signs out and departs

Figure 13b. Process for receiving ultrasound after Kaizen

you create an environment where work areas are self-explaining (visual), self-regulating and self-improving. "Products" from these white-collar "shop floors" are quite often repeatable and predictable, just like the goods produced in the factory. Process improvement in the white-collar realm yields great results.

The customers see the results and want more of your product or service because what is supposed to happen does happen, on time, every time, day or night. People do not wander or search for what they need to get the job done, because the tools are at their fingertips. There is no waiting and no delays, no wondering about what is supposed to get done and no secrets. Management is removing obstacles, barriers and detours. There are no injuries or extra things to do because the work is standardized. No waste and no red ink.

The point I'm trying to make is that white collar processes can and should be thought of as standard work just like blue collar or production work. They are made up of repeatable, predictable events that can be measured and improved. Too often white collar people think they are not candidates for Kaizen because what they do requires "creativity" or "spontaneous brainstorming."

As Womack and Jones point out in their book *Lean Thinking,* the service industry is an embarrassing and wasteful quagmire of batch and queue for which customers pay.[5]

An example by those authors is a typical airplane trip which consists of the following waste:

1. Nineteen organizations involved
2. Ten queues
3. Eight inspections
4. Baggage picked up and put down seven times
5. Thirteen hours elapsed for seven hours moving

We have all experienced frustrations like this. In the airport, in the hospital, in the office and in the factory, waste is all around us. The opportunity to be a world-class producer knocks on the doors of all businesses.

In summary, the greatest opportunity to drive down the cost of your product or service and increase the value of the company is to apply these principles across the entire system–a team of multi-skilled players.

XI.

Summary—Ten Lessons for World Class

Lesson 1: *People are the key to world class, not technology.*

Lesson 2: *If you are going uphill and taking one step at a time you are headed in the right direction.*

Lesson 3: *Without the understanding and knowledge of the Toyota Production System, you are a small ship in heavy fog without a reliable compass.*

Lesson 4: *Employee involvement is the foundation. Without it in place, you can't build a world-class production system.*

Lesson 5: *The methods, revolutions and thresholds that must be crossed to compete in the global market can not be accomplished from the bottom up: they have to start from the top down.*

Lesson 6: *The goal of a world-class production system can only be achieved with a JIT Promotion Office to help promote the process.*

LESSON 7: *If you're not simple, you can't be fast, and if you aren't fast, you can't win.*

LESSON 8: *Hiring consultants to come to your company, collect data, and feed it back to you with a strategy that requires you to spend money, add people and buy expensive machines and equipment means one thing . . . you are really stupid.*

LESSON 9: *In measuring progress toward the vision, metrics must be few, simple, meaningful and directly linked to visual targets in the workplace.*

LESSON 10: *The greatest opportunities to eliminate waste are in the corporate "waste"land: the office, the engineering floors, factories and the service industry.*

References

1. Womack, James and Daniel T. Jones. *Lean Thinking*. New York: Simon and Schuster, 1996, p. 27.
2. Lathrop, Phillip. "Where Your Wage Dollar Goes," *Healthcare Forum Journal*. July/August, 1991.
3. Blackburn, Joseph. "Time-Based Competition: White Collar Activities," *Business Horizons*. July/August, 1992, pp. 96–101.
4. *AHA Hospital Statistics*, 1991–92 edition.
5. Womack, James and Daniel T. Jones. *Lean Thinking*. New York: Simon and Schuster, 1996, p. 18.

Further Reading

Deming, W. Edwards. *Out of the Crisis.* Cambridge, Massachusetts: Massachusetts Institute of Technology, 1988.

Imai, Masaaki. *Kaizen, the Key to Japan's Competitive Success,* New York: Random House Business Division, 1986.

Ohno, Taiichi. *Toyota Production System: Beyond Large-Scale Production.* Portland, Oregon: Productivity Press, 1988.

Shingo, Shigeo. *Study of Toyota Production System (from Industrial Engineering Standpoint).* Tokyo: Japan Management Association, 1981.

Womack, James and Daniel T. Jones. *Lean Thinking,* New York: Simon and Schuster, 1996.

About the Author

John R. Black is Director of Lean Manufacturing Research and Development for Boeing Commercial Airplane Group (BCAG), reporting to the Executive Vice President, Airplane Components. He seeks out the world's best business innovations and works with Boeing leaders to get them implemented.

John is a pioneer of continuous quality improvement and lean manufacturing at The Boeing Company. Starting in 1980, he was instrumental in getting Boeing leaders to commit to the quality process. As an early student of Deming and Juran, Black was the first to introduce their ideas at Boeing. He helped benchmark leading companies in 1985, which led to the founding of the company's first two quality centers. He led the team that authored Boeing's first official quality plan, the development of initial quality training for 80,000 employees, and the first Managing Quality seminar, attended by 10,000 managers. He was responsible for the introduction and implementation of Total Quality Control with Malaysian Airlines in 1988.

In 1989, he pioneered the Japan Study Mission process for Boeing executives to visit and learn from world-class companies. He was a member of Boeing's first executive study mission to Japan in 1990, which was followed by six additional study missions, resulting in 100 of Boeing's top executives visiting nearly 25 top

Japanese companies. In 1991, he was instrumental in developing Boeing's World-Class Competitiveness course, sharing the results of these study missions with over 100,000 Boeing employees. He has participated in numerous Kaizen activities on the factory floor in Japan since 1995. He helped set the current strategy for Boeing's continued focus in implementing the Boeing Production System.

John R. Black, Director, Lean Manufacturing R & D, Boeing Commercial Airplane Group, 800 North 6th Street, Renton, WA 98055